DREAMS OF
Dragons
& DRAGON KIN

COLORING BOOK

RAVYNNE PHELAN

BLUE ANGEL®
PUBLISHING

Dreams of Dragons and Dragon Kin
Coloring Book

Copyright © 2016 Ravynne Phelan

All rights reserved.
Other than for personal use, no part of this book may be reproduced
in any way, in whole or part without the written consent
of the copyright holder or publisher.

Published by Blue Angel Publishing®
80 Glen Tower Drive, Glen Waverley
Victoria, Australia 3150
Email: info@blueangelonline.com
Website: www.blueangelonline.com

Line drawings created by Jenna Phelan

Blue Angel is a registered trademark of Blue Angel Gallery Pty. Ltd.

ISBN: 978-0-9871651-7-6

"If the sky could dream,
it would dream of dragons."

— Ilona Andrews, *Fate's Edge*

Introduction From Ravynne

I FIRST DREAMED OF DRAGONS when I was a young child. I dreamed of ancient, powerful, and magical creatures who flew through the heavens long before I had any exposure to them through stories or television. They existed within my mind, in a time before I could have possibly known what they were unless they truly existed.

And so I believe in them.

My first dragon was *my* invisible friend. My first dragon taught me how to fly in my dreams, and together we explored distant lands that, later, once I grew to adulthood, I discovered to be real and impossible for me to have known about. My faith in them is unshakeable. I believe in my dragon friends in the same way others believe in a god, goddess, or angel. They might only dwell within the realms of my mind, but I believe that we humans also exist within a God-mind, so it only stands to reason that dragons can and do live and thrive in my mind, and in the minds of others, in many universes that are just as real as our own.

They exist because I believe, *and I will always believe.*

Did they once dwell in this universe of ours, within the God-mind of the entity that believed us into being? I am certain they once did, and may continue to do so, for the God-mind is vast. Do some still hide within the deepest, most hidden reaches of this world? I believe they do. Dragons are born of stardust and the elements. They are inherently drawn to and tied to the very things from which they are made. They sleep within the earth, dreaming of Gaia. Are some right in front of us, hidden in plain sight, in a form that we frail and mortal humans are less likely to fear? I believe they are. Dragons are shapeshifters, and can become whatever they choose to be. All I will say is that if you are a cat lover, you will know dragon energy on an intimate level. Look into their eyes and you will know that dragons exist, for they are dragon kin.

So if dragons exist, what is their purpose? Why, if they are good and benevolent, do so many stories paint them as evil?

Dragons are not rapacious devourers of virgins. They are not all hoarders of treasure made mad by their lust for gold, although some do love their shiny pretties. The dragons we have been taught to fear are metaphors for human behavior. Are dragons all good and benevolent? No, but we humans fear them, not because they are evil, but because we do not understand them. We fear them because they are manifestations of pure power, who can teach us to be powerful as well, if we are willing to learn. They are ancient, immortal, and so much wiser than we are. They are all that we seek to become, but fear to be, and so instead of learning from them, we destroy them. We make them the mirrors of our fear, our lust, our greed, and ignorance, and take up arms against them.

I do not fear them. Nor do I fear being thought of as eccentric or crazy because I believe in them. My dragons taught me to fly in my dreams. They taught me to believe in my dreams. They taught me to be less afraid. They taught me to believe in myself in the same manner I believe in them. They taught me to see a bigger picture, and to embrace a rainbow of color instead of black and white. They taught me that while color might, at times, offer less contrast, it shapes our reality and provides us with more understanding. They also taught me to believe in the intangible, the unseen, the unknown, and to know that all is infinite and all things are possible.

I may not have wings, and, no, I cannot fly, but my dragons taught me to soar, and I move through life with the awareness that I can achieve anything I set my heart, mind, and soul to accomplishing, if I am willing to see, understand, and embrace the full power of my choices.

I am the person I am because I believe in dragons. I am the person I am because dragons believe in me.

This coloring book is a celebration of dragon and dragon-like energy. It is a product of my imagination, and my imagination is a doorway into a multiverse where dragons dwell. Step through. Explore. See them as I do, and by giving them color, give them life, as I do.

Believe, and make magic.

Protector of the Magic I

Watercolor and ink on 100% cotton
watercolor paper
11.75" x 16.75"   © 2005

This was the first of several versions of this painting. Every version depicts a dragon watching over the young Tree of Magic – the tree from which all magic comes. The seeds that fall from the tree drift out into the worlds of all and merge with all new souls. When a soul carries a seed of magic within, it will hear the Song of Magic. To hear the Song is to believe and to be connected to the threads of magic that weave through all and everything.

Whist – Be Patient

Acrylic on 100% cotton watercolor paper
5" x 7"   © 2010

Whist, this wee dragon hatchling, was painted for inclusion in *Messenger Oracle*. He was indeed a patient little dragon, for life was a little busy at the time, and it took me an unusually long period of several weeks to complete this very small painting.

Water Drake – Ace of Water

Acrylic on 100% cotton watercolor paper
8.5" x 11.5"   © 2012

Water Drake was painted for inclusion in the *Dreams of Gaia Tarot*. He now is the Ace of Water in the deck, and represents new emotions and new love.

The Sky Watcher

Acrylic on 100% cotton watercolor paper
11.75" x 16.75"   © 2014

Sky Watcher is one of my feline dragons. He sits with his face turned toward the heavens, listening to the songs of the cosmic dragons that move through the skies above.

Dragon Dancer

Graphite on drawing paper
11.75" x 16.75"   © 2014

This is one of many drawings that I have completed that still waits to be painted. It was a design concept for the Queens in the *Dreams of Gaia Tarot* that was ultimately replaced by the final design featured in the deck.

The Dragon's Door

Acrylic on canvas
20" x 30" © 2014

"The Dragon's Door" is yet another reworking of an older painting. The original version depicted a small dragon, who watched over and protected the doorway into his wizard friend's chambers. This later version has a more symbolic message. The dragon's message is that we are capable of all we seek to accomplish. Any obstacle in our way – a door, for example – is an illusion. While we are not always responsible for the obstacles we find in our path, we do give them power and make them more solid than they are. The door is an illusion. Go through and discover what awaits you.

Abundance

Acrylic on 100% cotton watercolor paper
11.75" x 16.75" © 2013

Over the years, I have painted a number of dragons that were based on Celtic gods and goddesses. The dragon in this particular image was going to be my Dagda. However, he decided otherwise, and instead insisted that he be used for the Abundance card from the *Dreams of Gaia Tarot*.

Cradle the Moon –
Nurture All That You Love

Acrylic on 100% cotton watercolor paper
11.75" x 16.75"   © 2012

I believe that every planet has a cosmic dragon watching over it, protecting it, nurturing it, loving it. For every "feminine" planet, there is a "masculine" dragon paired with it. "Cradle the Moon" symbolizes that pairing, and the protective, nurturing role of the cosmic dragon. The message is simple – nurture all that you love. Keep it safe. Cherish it. This artwork was later used in the *Messenger Oracle* for the Nurture All That You Love card.

Daughter of the Moon
and Stars

Acrylic on 100% cotton watercolor paper
8.5" x 11.5" © 2014

This beautiful dragon, who appears in her humanoid form, was painted in celebration of a milestone achieved on my Facebook page! She was given away in thanks to those who have supported me over the years.

Dia Griene

Acrylic on 100% cotton watercolor paper
11" x 14"   © 2007

Dia Griene is one of my "Celtic Gods as Dragons"
series. Dia Griene was the daughter of the Sun.

Grollup

Graphite on 100% cotton watercolor paper
8.5" x 11.5" © 2008

I can be just a little bit of a "mad scientist" at times.
I often find myself sitting and pondering how a
particular creature would appear if I were to mix just
a little bit of this animal or that with dragon. Grollup
is part green tree frog, and part dragon. Sometimes,
I find myself feeling sad that they can only be real
inside my head.

The Beekeeper

Acrylic on 100% cotton watercolor paper
11.75" x 16.75" © 2014

The Beekeeper is a gentle creature, who often hides in lavender bushes, where it watches over the bees as they come and go. He is most interested in keeping our bee friends safe, as his kind know all too well how destructive humans can be, and how blind they can be to the symbiotic nature of their relationship with the planet and all that dwells upon the earth with them. Everything exists for a reason. All has a purpose. The Beekeeper seeks to teach humanity that they must protect and nurture all, because all, especially the bees, are necessary to humanity's continued survival.

Caduceus

Graphite on drawing paper
11.75" x 16.75"   © 2005

"Caduceus" was a design with a message I was just beginning to explore on a spiritual level. She was going to be painted in rainbow hues with just a little bit of black and white at the extreme edges of the wings. At the time, I had come to a place where I could no longer subscribe to a dualistic good-versus-bad form of spirituality. The notion that a particular behavior or trait was either harmful or beneficial seemed just a little too cut and dried. The reality is that something that is good and healing for one may be harmful and poisonous to another. What someone perceives to be good, another might, from their different perspective, see as being destructive. There are no correct answers. Instead, there are many answers. There is no right or true path, only the path that serves you best. Caduceus was going to symbolize wholeness but I have not yet found the time to paint her, and she eventually evolved and shifted. The dragons were used in the Self card, and the central figure was used in the Union card of my *Dreams of Gaia Tarot*. Both cards embody the overall message that we are here to become whole, not to divide and separate.

Gaia's Protector

Graphite on drawing paper
8.5" x 11.5"   © 2015

This particular dragon is a concept drawing for a much larger dragon painting with body attached. He is a big leafy beast that is yet to be painted, but represents one of Gaia's many dragon protectors. Yes, he is a bit of a metaphor for all those who actively serve to protect our planet's forest from further destruction. His energy resides in all of us who love the wilds and believe they should be left alone.

Ten of Earth

Acrylic on 100% cotton watercolor paper
8.5" x 11.5"   © 2012

The Ten of Earth card from the *Dreams of Gaia Tarot* symbolizes all aspects of life coming together as a whole. Career, home, family – all are in harmony. Years of dedicated service to family, career, and community have reaped the highest of rewards – the love, respect, and trust of family and peers. This love, respect, and trust are a reflection of what is felt within, and inspire a sense of wellbeing and connectedness that enables one to move through life with both grace and ease.

Gryphon

Graphite on drawing paper
11.75" x 16.75" © 2015

Okay, I know. It's a gryphon, and a gryphon is not a dragon. But I cannot help but feel that they are kin to dragons and energetically the same in many ways – fierce, protective, wise …

Footstep

Acrylic on 100% cotton watercolor paper
Size: 11.75" x 16.75" © 2015

The creature depicted in this artwork is yet another dragon-animal chimaera. It is an earth spirit, bound to the earth by love. Its message is simple. Keep your footsteps upon this land both light and gentle. Respect and care for Gaia and her children, lest the spirits bound to this planet turn against you. Dragons have a fondness for humanity, but their first love is for Gaia.

Rebirth Awaits

Acrylic on 100% cotton watercolor paper
11.75" x 16.75" © 2015

Oh, I did it again, didn't I? I snuck another "it's not a dragon" into the book, but again, the phoenix has powerful, dragon-like energy. After all, it is an eternal being, symbolic of death and rebirth. Dragons are much the same.

Sphynx

Graphite on drawing paper
8.5" x 11.5" © 2016

I am a cat lover. It would be pointless for me to deny that I love cats and have the intention of becoming a crazy cat lady as I grow older. If you don't like cats, then I am sorry, but I cannot be friends with you. If my cats do not like you, then again, my apologies, but I cannot share space with you. I am owned, body, mind, and spirit by them, because, to me, cats are the very essence of dragon. They are how dragons appear to us in this world because we are so afraid of their "truer" form. With that being said, I have, for a long time, been quite fascinated by the Sphynx breed. Their appearance is so very striking. They are so very cat-like, but also so different that it sets them apart. And because of my fascination, I was inspired to reveal the Sphynx cat's draconic nature.

I Am

Acrylic on canvas
24" x 30" © 2012

The dragon depicted in "I Am" is a being of great and ancient power. He is one of the first dragons to be born of the Void, and his message is simple: You are not the words with which you define and label yourself. You are so much more. You are a creature of infinite potential and possibility. In the simplest terms, you are, and that is enough.

Chimaera

Acrylic on 100% cotton watercolor paper
5.5" x 8.5"   © 2014

This beautiful creature is a lion dragon chimaera – a
golden creature of sun and flame.

Dragon Mask

Graphite on drawing paper
5" x 7"   © 2011

The original concept behind the drawing was that we humans have a habit of only looking at the surface of things. More often than not, we see only the faces people wear when they are out in public or at a social engagement. We see the book cover, but rarely glimpse more than a few pages inside the book. There is nothing wrong with this, as long as we accept that what we see is often just a glimpse and not the entirety. For all we believe we know, there is so much more we do not. We have to take the time to look beyond the masks and learn more about the multifaceted beings that dwell behind them.

My Pretty Blues

Watercolor on 100% cotton watercolor paper
11.75" x 16.75"   © 2005

Oh, he's a feisty wee dragon. I would not want to upset him and be swatted for my transgressions. And swat you he will if you even think to take any of his pretty blues. Yes, this wee dragon is a hoarder of treasures. Like an Australian bowerbird, he collects his pretty blues in order to impress potential mates. He guards them jealously, because the loss of a single pretty blue might reduce his chances to impress.

The First Dragon

Watercolor on 100% cotton watercolor paper
11.75" x 16.75"   © 2007

This painting is a very personal piece. The dragon depicted is the dragon who taught me to fly within my dreams. He is the first. My first. My best "imaginary" friend and dragon protector. Many have come to visit with me since then, but he is my first love, and I will always love him the most.

Fire Drake – Ace of Fire

Graphite on drawing paper
8.5" x 11.5"   © 2012

"Fire Drake," like "Water Drake," was painted for inclusion in my tarot deck. The tarot version is a little different, but still very much the leonine dragon I envisioned.

The Gift

Acrylic and colored pencil on 100% cotton
watercolor paper
11.75" x 16.75"   © 2009

"The Gift" was painted to share my painting process
– or the one I used at that stage of my career – with
everyone. A walk-through was created for publication
in my art book, *Dreams of Magic*.

The Matriarch

Acrylic on 100% cotton watercolor paper
11.75" x 16.75" © 2014

The Matriarch is another old and ancient being. I have never learned why, but female cosmic dragons are rare, so the few that exist are the mothers to many. All dragons, other than the first who were born of the Void when the universe came to be, are born of the few matriarchs like her. Scarred by time and battles a-many, the Matriarch is very crone-like in nature and energy. She does not tolerate ignorance and foolishness. Nor does she follow the ways of others. She certainly does not "do as she is told." The Matriarch bows her head to no one, except her creator.

Starborn

Watercolor and Graphite on 100% cotton
watercolor paper
5" x 7"   © 2008

Dragon or human, we are both made of star stuff. We
are both born of the stars. We are "starborn."

Entwined

Acrylic on 100% cotton watercolor paper
5.5" x 8.5"   © 2008

There was no great thought or feeling that motivated me to paint this one other than to gauge and measure my improvement as an artist. This is version two of this concept. The first was painted in 2003 and, at the time, I used watercolors. This time around, I used acrylics and a different color palette. I have to admit that I have never been 100% satisfied with the outcome of the two versions of this painting, and so there may eventually be a third, and, because I have evolved and changed, the line work foundation of the new version will also change. I like to test myself. I enjoy seeing how much and in what ways my work has changed over the years. I usually find that when I take the time to revisit the paintings I was not completely satisfied with, I eventually get it right and come up with a version where the picture that is in my mind can finally be reproduced by my hands.

Flower – Respect Your Boundaries

Acrylic on 100% cotton watercolor paper
8.5" x 11.5"   © 2011

Flower is a gentle dragon, and one of the few female dragons I have painted in dragon form. There is a common theme among the females of dragon kind, and that is to honor one's self. Flower's message is a very simple one – respect your boundaries. If you say, "No," do not allow others to believe that your no is a yes. Have the courage to remain resolute, because if you are unwilling to stand true to your own convictions, nobody else will. If you set boundaries, and then do not abide by those boundaries yourself, nobody else will.

Time of Rebirth

Acrylic on canvas
20" x 30"   © 2012

Yeah, I know. I did it again. It's not a dragon, but 2012 was a very important year for me. I went through a lot of internal growth, finally accepting things about myself that I could not change and determining what was important to me and what was not. My dragon friends played their part in helping me reach that point in much the same way another person's "angels" and "spirit guides" would. So while this is a phoenix, it was painted because of my dragons and their love for me.

The Light Weaver

Acrylic on canvas
24" x 36"   © 2013

The Light Weaver is a creature of love and light. He is one of the first. One of the ancients. He comes to show us the light within us all, and to remind us that we are creatures of infinite potential if we create with the power and purity of love.

Spitfire

Acrylic on 100% cotton watercolor paper
8.5" x 11.5"   © 2015

One of the birds I love is the diminutive blue wren. It is so small, and yet there are times when I think this bold little being would spit flames at people if it could. Instead of flying away, the feisty ball of feathers, will turn and chatter in defiance, as if challenging those who come too close to do battle. Of course, after seeing this behavior in my own garden, I was inspired to depict this little beastie as a dragon, and even before the paint was dry, I named him Spitfire.

Sentinel

Acrylic on 100% cotton watercolor paper
11.75" x 16.75"   © 2015

Not really a dragon, but this winged wolf is draconic in energy and nature. Like most dragons, he is protective. He stands as sentinel, watching for anything that might bring harm or destruction to those he loves.

From the White

Acrylic on 100% cotton watercolor paper
11.75" x 16.75"   © 2015

In more recent years, I have been inspired to do less figurative art and more totemic works. In part, that desire was inspired by a need for change after years of painting figurative illustrations for the tarot. I envisioned this particular piece as a back tattoo.

The Naga Transforms

Graphite on drawing paper
11.75" x 16.75" © 2015

The Naga is a mythical, giant, serpent-like dragon. In India, the Nagas are believed to be nature spirits associated with rain, rivers, streams, wells, and lakes. Because of their strong links to water, they are also associated with transformation, fertility, and abundance. They are the rain-bringers, and rain transforms the land. However, the Nagas are also associated with famine and disasters, for should you displease or harm a Naga, they may withhold the rains and, in turn, bring drought.

Gift From the Void –
You Were Born To Create

Acrylic on canvas
20" x 30" © 2011

This dark and powerful creature came to me in a dream. He told me that he represents the Void that dwells within each and every one of us. That Void is the birthplace of all that we imagine and create. He was a little intimidating at first, but in my dream I could not resist reaching up and scratching his face. He purred in response in a very cat-like manner. It was a purr that earned him the nickname of "Fluffy Face" and made me want to scratch him again every time I looked upon his face.

The Gatekeeper

Digital
23.4" x 16.5"   © 2016

The Gatekeeper might appear to be a little gruff, but he is a very gentle and protective dragon. He stands at the entrance of all portals, preventing less than nice energies and entities from entering our realities.

The Red Queen

Acrylic on 100% cotton watercolor paper
11.75" x 16.75"   © 2015

The Red Queen is in her humanoid form. Scarred by
time, she stands proud, knowing that her scars make
her more beautiful.

Mistress of the Wells

Acrylic on canvas
24" x 36"   © 2012

Mistress of the Wells has a very complex meaning. First, she represents the need to not hold on to our emotions, to experience them, and to then allow them to flow away. Second, she represents the relationship between dragons and the natural world. Dragons are often tied to the land in a very elemental way. Volcanoes, forests, waterways, mountain tops … these are all places where you will often find a dragon.

The Winged Drackalope

Acrylic on 100% cotton watercolor paper
11.75" x 16.75"   © 2015

Have you ever heard of a jackalope? A jackalope is mythological creature from Northern America. It is described as being like a jackrabbit with antelope horns. It is a chimaera. The winged drackalope evolves this mythological creature just a little more. It is given the wings of a dragonfly and the frills and tail of a dragon. It becomes the winged drackalope.

Soulmates – Show That You Care

Acrylic on 100% cotton watercolor paper
11.75" x 16.75"   © 2009

"Soulmates" symbolizes a bond that transcends all. All too often, people regard a soulmate as a romantic pairing, when, in reality, a soulmate can be anyone with whom you have a relationship that feels as if it has always been. It is a bond between two souls that transcends time, species, race, and gender. All you see is the soul that you have loved, do love, and will always love. Your soulmate may come to you as a lover, but they may also come to you as a friend, a sibling, a parent, or even, on occasion, an enemy. You are bound to each other by love, and return to each other in order to inspire growth and increase wisdom. You may spend a lifetime looking for each other, only to have a few minutes together. Regardless of who they are, or the skin that they wear, you will know, because you have known them forever.

"Soulmates" later evolved and became the illustration for the Show That You Care card in *Messenger Oracle*.

Cernunnos – Be Strong

Acrylic on 100% cotton watercolor paper
11" x 14"   © 2009

"Cernunnos" was another from my "Celtic Gods as Dragons" series, and one painting that has had several evolutions. The original image was drawn back in 2003, and was painted digitally. When I moved from using the computer, first to watercolors, and then to acrylics, I repainted it, and then a few years later painted it again so I could see how my work had changed over the years. The current version will likely be the last, because he now illustrates perfectly the horned nature god of the Celts.

Pipsqueak

Acrylic on 100% cotton watercolor paper
8.5" x 11.5" © 2010

Pipsqueak is another of my imaginings. He's a little bit rabbit, a little bit lion, a little bit dragonfly, and a lot of dragon. He is incredibly cute, and if I could make this little critter real, I would. He stands about six inches high, and when the light hits him just right, he becomes a rainbow of iridescent hues. He is gentle, playful, and loves nothing more than to rummage around in the grass and leaves, looking for bugs and beetles to munch on. He would be the perfect magical companion.

If only …

The Wisdom Keeper

Acrylic on 100% cotton watercolor paper
5.5" x 8.5"   © 2014

Yet another cat-turned-dragon. The Wisdom Keeper is part panther and part dragon, and a very wise being. He sees all, but also accepts that the more he understands, the less he knows.

One – We Are All Connected

Acrylic on canvas
20" x 30" © 2012

In my humble opinion, this painting says it all. It illustrates the importance of humanity in the grand scheme of things. See the painting as representative of a totem pole of sorts, in order of value. At the top there are trees and plants. While some need animals and birds to spread their seeds, the plant kingdom does not need either animals or humans to exist in order for them to survive. Animals rank second on the totem pole, for while they need plants and other animals in order to sustain their lives, they do not need humans. We do not add to their existence. In fact, we do nothing but take from both the plant and animal kingdoms. Which is why we are at the bottom. We cannot survive without the plants and animals that we share this world with. Without them, we perish, and yet so many humans still believe that humanity holds dominion over all.

It is time for humans to accept and understand that we have a symbiotic relationship with this planet and all of its inhabitants. If we harm the planet, destroy the forests, and kill all of the animals, even if we do so simply by over-breeding, we destroy ourselves. We are all connected.

The Morrighan

Acrylic on 100% cotton watercolor paper
11.75" x 16.75"   © 2009

"The Morrighan" – Queen of shadows, blood, and war – and another from the "Celtic Gods as Dragons" series. She is the one who decides the warrior's fate and whether he will walk away from the battlefield with his life.

The Sky Singer

Graphite on drawing paper
11.75" x 16.75"   © 2014

"The Sky Singer" is a partner piece to "The Sky Watcher." The Sky Watcher watches the skies above, searching for his cosmic dragon kin, while the Sky Singer calls them home.

The Keeper of Wisdom

Acrylic on 100% cotton watercolor paper
11.75" x 16.75"   © 2015

The Keeper of Wisdom was inspired by Wan Shi Tong, an owl spirit from the film *The Last Airbender*. I have always loved owls and dragons, but this is the first time I have painted them as one. It had always been my intent to do so, but life is full, and so it was a union that did not come to be until I was reminded by Wan Shi Tong of my intent to make it happen.

Myst Weaver

Acrylic on 100% cotton watercolor paper
8.5" x 11.5"   © 2014

Myst Weaver is another animal-dragon spirit. Where he walks, the mists follow. He is one of those magical creatures you will glimpse out of the corner of your eye, but who disappears when you turn to get a second look. You might sometimes see what appears to be a hint of a tail or a flash of wings, but the mist hides the weaver from view before you can determine or confirm what it is that you actually saw.

Phoenix

Acrylic on 100% cotton watercolor paper
11.75" x 16.75" © 2015

Why is the Phoenix important to me? During my life,
I seem to have become many different people. Those
people are always alike, but after key moments that
have altered my perception and understanding of the
world, I have become someone who is very different
to the person I was prior to those moments. I have
been transformed. Reborn. For better or worse, I am
no longer the same. All that I was has been undone,
and I can only be who I am in the moment, until, in
the next moment, I become something more, and I
am reborn again. My dragons, having lives so very
long that they appear eternal, understand this living
rebirth, for it is how they are reborn. They experience,
they learn, they are transformed, and sometimes the
changes within are so fundamental, they are changed
forever.

For more information on this
or any Blue Angel Publishing release,
please visit our website at:
www.blueangelonline.com